CONTENTS

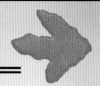

WHAT IS A BRACHIOSAURUS?

BRACHIOSAURUS MEANS 'ARM LIZARD'

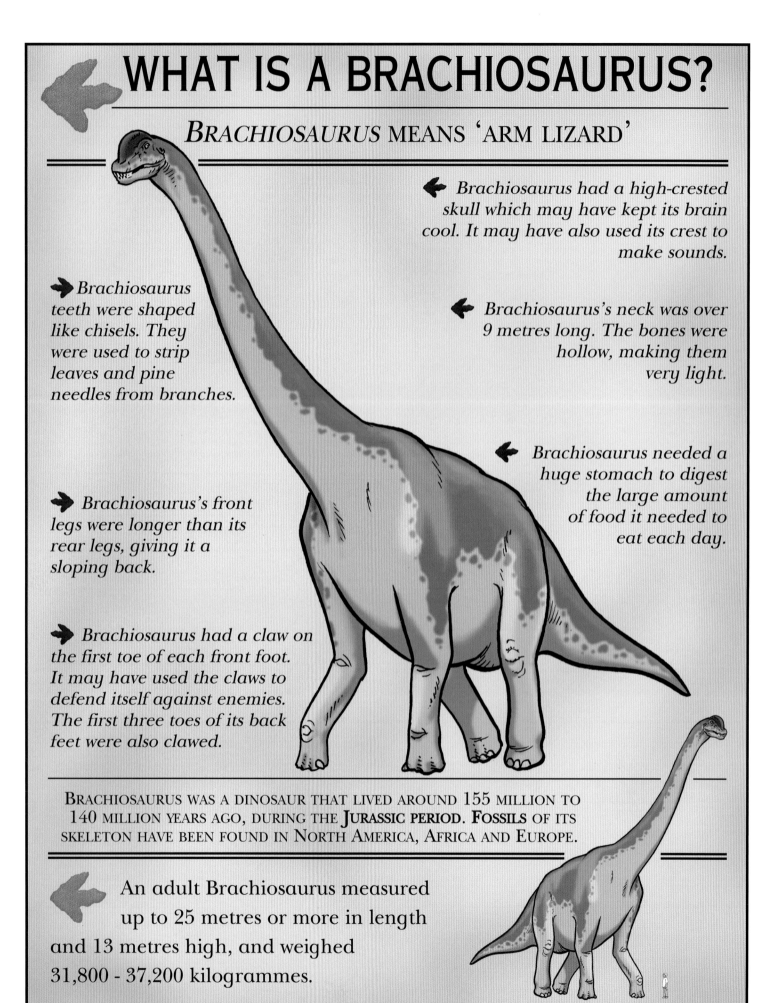

Brachiosaurus had a high-crested skull which may have kept its brain cool. It may have also used its crest to make sounds.

Brachiosaurus teeth were shaped like chisels. They were used to strip leaves and pine needles from branches.

Brachiosaurus's neck was over 9 metres long. The bones were hollow, making them very light.

Brachiosaurus needed a huge stomach to digest the large amount of food it needed to eat each day.

Brachiosaurus's front legs were longer than its rear legs, giving it a sloping back.

Brachiosaurus had a claw on the first toe of each front foot. It may have used the claws to defend itself against enemies. The first three toes of its back feet were also clawed.

BRACHIOSAURUS WAS A DINOSAUR THAT LIVED AROUND 155 MILLION TO 140 MILLION YEARS AGO, DURING THE JURASSIC PERIOD. FOSSILS OF ITS SKELETON HAVE BEEN FOUND IN NORTH AMERICA, AFRICA AND EUROPE.

An adult Brachiosaurus measured up to 25 metres or more in length and 13 metres high, and weighed 31,800 - 37,200 kilogrammes.

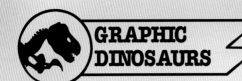

presents

BRACHIOSAURUS

THE LONG-LIMBED DINOSAUR!

ILLUSTRATED BY TERRY RILEY

BOOK HOUSE

Graphic Dinosaurs Brachiosaurus
was produced by
David West Children's Books
7 Princeton Court
55 Felsham Road
London SW15 1AZ

Designed and written by Rob Shone
Illustrated by Terry Riley
Consultant: Steve Parker, Senior Scientific Fellow, Zoological Society of London
Cover designed by Rob Walker

First published in the UK in MMX by Book House,
an imprint of The Salariya Book Company Ltd.,
25, Marlborough Place, Brighton BN1 1UB

Please visit the Salariya Book Company at:
www.book-house.co.uk

1 3 5 7 9 8 6 4 2

ISBN: 978-1-907184-02-4 (HB)
ISBN: 978-1-907184-03-1 (PB)

A CIP catalogue record for this book is available from the British Library.

Photographic credits:
5t, Ninjatacoshell; 5m, species_snob; 5b, Rob Inh00d; 30, Axel Mauruszat.
Library of Congress Cataloging-in-Publication Data

Printed and bound in China.

Printed on paper from sustainable sources.

WATER DINOSAUR

When fossilised bones of Brachiosaurus were first found, it was thought that it had lived in lakes, its huge weight being supported by the water. Now scientists know that Brachiosaurus could not have lived like that. The force of the water on its chest would have stopped it from breathing properly.

Brachiosauruses would have fed on tall plants like these Araucarias.

Brachiosaurus's neck was 9 metres long but was made up of just 12 bones.

For many years, the nostrils of a Brachiosaurus were thought to be on top of its crest. Now, however, scientists think they were near the end of its snout.

FEEDING HABITS

Brachiosauruses were sauropods, a type of dinosaur that ate plants, walked on four legs and had a long neck and tail. Brachiosauruses moved in herds, using their long necks to reach plants too high for other dinosaurs to feed on. To help them digest tough pine needles and ferns, Brachiosauruses swallowed stones (gastroliths) which ground the food in their stomach.

The present-day animal that is most like a Brachiosaurus is the giraffe. It uses its long neck to reach leaves from the tops of trees.

PART ONE... **THE BREAKOUT**

IT IS ANOTHER HOT AFTERNOON AS A BRACHIOSAURUS HERD MOVES SLOWLY THROUGH THE FOREST. ONE FEMALE IS LAYING HER EGGS. SHE HAS NOT BUILT A NEST BUT LAYS THEM IN A LINE AS SHE WALKS ALONG. FINALLY, SHE LAYS HER LAST EGG. SHE DOES NOT LOOK TO SEE WHERE IT HAS LANDED AND DOES NOT STAY TO CARE FOR IT. SHE WILL BE FAR AWAY WHEN IT HATCHES.

THE GROWING BRACHIOSAURUS IN THAT EGG FACES MANY DANGERS. IT COULD BE CRUSHED UNDER THE FOOT OF A LARGE DINOSAUR, FALL PREY TO AN EGG THIEF OR BE KILLED BY COLD WEATHER.

AFTER MANY WEEKS, THE BRACHIOSAURUS IS READY TO HATCH. THE EGG'S THICK SHELL MAKES IT HARD TO BREAK INTO BUT EASY FOR A HATCHLING TO BREAK OUT. SOON CRACKS APPEAR ON THE EGG'S SURFACE.

WITH EFFORT, THE TINY BRACHIOSAURUS LIFTS HER HEAD OUT OF HER EGGSHELL HOME.

THE HATCHLING FREES HERSELF FROM HER EGG. THERE ARE MORE EMPTY EGGS NEARBY, BUT NO OTHER HATCHLINGS. SHE DOES NOT FEEL SAFE, SO SHE HIDES. HER MARKINGS HELP HER BLEND IN WITH THE SURROUNDING PLANTS.

SHE IS HUNGRY AND BEGINS TO MUNCH ON THE TENDER FERNS THAT GROW ALL AROUND HER. SHE WILL DECIDE WHAT TO DO NEXT ONCE SHE HAS FED.

THE SMALL BRACHIOSAURUS FEELS BRAVER NOW THAT SHE HAS EATEN. SHE WANDERS DEEP INTO THE FOREST. TREES TOWER ABOVE HER AND FERNS GROW THICKLY IN THE DAMP GROUND.

THE BRACHIOSAURUS CLIMBS A SMALL PILE OF DEAD LEAVES AND FERNS.

THERE IS MOVEMENT BENEATH HER FEET.

A TINY HEAD POKES THROUGH THE DEAD LEAVES.

GNAHHH!!

THE FIRST HEAD IS FOLLOWED BY A SECOND AND A THIRD.

THE BRACHIOSAURUS HAS WALKED ONTO A HAPLOCANTHOSAURUS NEST AND THE EGGS HAVE STARTED TO HATCH. SHE IS SOON CIRCLED BY SMALL HATCHLINGS. HAPLOCANTHOSAURUSES ARE LONG-NECKED PLANT EATERS LIKE THE BRACHIOSAURUSES.

WHEN THE HAPLOCANTHOSAURUS EGGS WERE LAID, THEIR PARENTS HID THEM UNDER VEGETATION AND THEN LEFT. THERE IS NOT ENOUGH FOOD FOR THE ADULTS TO STAY IN ONE PLACE FOR VERY LONG.

THE BRACHIOSAURUS TURNS TO LEAVE WHEN...

AARRK!!

RARRK!!

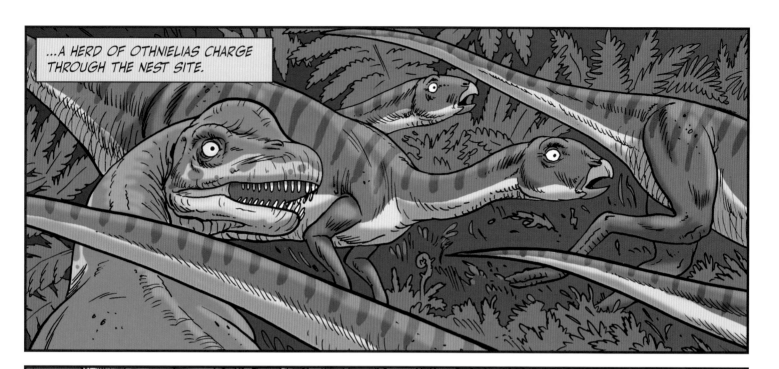

...A HERD OF OTHNIELIAS CHARGE THROUGH THE NEST SITE.

THE SMALL PLANT EATERS ARE BEING HUNTED BY A TANYCOLAGREUS.

THE HAPLOCANTHOSAURUS HATCHLINGS SCATTER INTO THE FERNS.

GGRRRRAAHH!!

THE MEAT-EATING TANYCOLAGREUS CATCHES AN UNLUCKY OTHNIELIA. THE BRACHIOSAURUS SLIPS AWAY UNSEEN.

SHRAAHHK...

THE BRACHIOSAURUS IS ALONE AGAIN - BUT NOT FOR LONG.

THERE IS A SHADOWY SHAPE IN THE FERNS AHEAD.

THE HIDDEN ANIMAL MOVES INTO THE LIGHT. IT IS ANOTHER BRACHIOSAURUS HATCHLING.

THERE ARE OTHER YOUNG BRACHIOSAURUSES FEEDING IN THE **UNDERGROWTH**. THEY ALL HATCHED FROM THE SAME GROUP OF EGGS. THE SMALL HATCHLING HAS FOUND HER BROTHERS AND SISTERS.

PART TWO... JURASSIC GIANTS

IT HAS BEEN A YEAR SINCE THE SMALL BRACHIOSAURUS JOINED HER BROTHERS AND SISTERS. NOW ONLY THREE OF THEM ARE LEFT. THE OTHERS HAVE NOT SURVIVED. IN THE PAST YEAR, SHE HAS GROWN TO OVER 3 METRES LONG AND IS TALL ENOUGH TO FEED ON TREE FERNS AND CYCADS. SHE AND HER TWO REMAINING BROTHERS ARE FEEDING ON CYCADS WHEN...

...A MARSHOSAURUS DASHES OUT OF THE UNDERGROWTH.

THE BRACHIOSAURUSES DO NOT HAVE TIME TO ESCAPE. THE MEAT EATER RACES STRAIGHT AT THEM...

...BUT DOES NOT STOP. IT IS SCARED AND IS RUNNING AWAY FROM SOMETHING.

A HERD OF CAMARASAURUSES BURSTS FROM THE JUNGLE. THE MARSHOSAURUS HAD ATTACKED A YOUNG CAMARASAURUS AND THE ADULTS HAD GROUPED TOGETHER TO PROTECT IT. THEY ARE STILL ANGRY AND ARE TRYING TO CHASE THE MEAT EATER AWAY.

BROUAHH!!

ROUAHH!!

THE CAMARASAURUSES MOVE ON. THEY ARE STILL ANGRY AND SEE EVERYTHING AS A THREAT, EVEN THE BRACHIOSAURUSES.

A SHORT DISTANCE AWAY, THE MARSHOSAURUS TRIES TO STAND. ITS LEG IS HURT FROM THE FALL. IT SEES THE BRACHIOSAURUSES AND LIMPS AFTER THEM. EVEN WITH AN INJURED LEG, HE WILL EASILY CATCH UP WITH THEM, AND THERE ARE NO ADULTS NEARBY TO SAVE THEM.

FOR THE SECOND TIME THAT DAY, THE BRACHIOSAURUSES SEE THE MEAT EATER COMING TOWARDS THEM. THIS TIME HE WILL NOT RUN PAST THEM. THE BRACHIOSAURUSES RUN AS FAST AS THEY CAN.

THE BRACHIOSAURUSES DO NOT RUN FAR. A HERD OF SUPERSAURUSES IS WALKING ACROSS THEIR PATH.

WITH THE MARSHOSAURUS CLOSE BEHIND THEM, THE BRACHIOSAURUSES MUST GO FORWARD.

THE SUPERSAURUSES HARDLY NOTICE THE THREE LITTLE DINOSAURS AS THEY **DODGE** BETWEEN THE GIGANTIC LEGS.

PART THREE... FEEDING TIME

A DEAD STEGOSAURUS HAS BEEN IN THE FOREST FOR SEVERAL DAYS. DERMESTID BEETLES SWARM OVER THE DINOSAUR'S BODY, LAYING THEIR EGGS. WHEN THEY HATCH, THE GRUBS WILL DIG INTO THE DINOSAUR BONES WHERE THEY WILL FEED AND GROW.

MEANWHILE, A PAIR OF COELURUSES CAREFULLY APPROACH THE CARCASS.

THE SMALL MEAT EATERS ARE HOPING TO GET A FREE MEAL.

NOT FAR AWAY, A TORVOSAURUS WATCHES THEM. THE KILL BELONGS TO HIM AND HE DOES NOT LIKE TO SHARE.

HE ROARS AT THE THIEVES, WHO RUN.

ROUUAARRRHH!

CLOSE BY, THE YOUNG BRACHIOSAURUS AND HER BROTHERS ARE FEEDING. THEY HAVE BEEN WITH THE HERD FOR THREE YEARS NOW AND ARE TALL ENOUGH TO REACH THE LEAVES OF SMALLER TREES. THE TORVOSAURUS PAYS NO ATTENTION TO THEM. HE IS TOO BUSY USING HIS SHARP CURVED TEETH TO TEAR OFF LARGE CHUNKS OF MEAT, WHICH HE GULPS DOWN WHOLE.

IN ONE OF THE PINE TREES, A SMALL MAMMAL HAS CAUGHT A MAYFLY. LIKE ALL MAMMALS, IT HAS FUR AND GIVES BIRTH TO LIVE YOUNG. IT ALSO HAS SPECIAL TEETH - FRONT ONES FOR BITING AND GNAWING AND BACK ONES FOR CRUSHING AND GRINDING. THE YOUNG BRACHIOSAURUS, LIKE MOST DINOSAURS, HAS ONLY ONE TYPE OF TOOTH.

GERRUNCHH!!

SHE USES HER CHISEL-SHAPED TEETH TO STRIP BRANCHES OF THEIR LEAVES. LIKE ALL BRACHIOSAURUSES, SHE CAN ONLY MOVE HER JAWS UP AND DOWN. SHE CANNOT CHEW HER FOOD.

20

WHEN SHE IS FULLY GROWN, SHE WILL NEED TO EAT 181 KILOGRAMMES OF PLANT MATTER EVERY DAY.

WHILE THE YOUNG BRACHIOSAURUS FEEDS ON THE TREES, A HAPLOCANTHOSAURUS CROPS THE LEAVES OF TREE FERNS AND CYCADS. IT IS A SAUROPOD LIKE THE BRACHIOSAURUS BUT CANNOT LIFT ITS HEAD MUCH HIGHER THAN ITS BACK.

ON THE FOREST FLOOR, A GARGOYLEOSAURUS BUSILY NIBBLES ON LOW-GROWING FERNS AND CYCADS. THESE ARMOURED DINOSAURS BITE OFF FERN LEAVES WITH THEIR BEAKS AND USE THEIR BACK TEETH TO SLICE THEM UP.

WHILE FEEDING, THE BRACHIOSAURUS ACCIDENTALLY DISTURBS A GROUP OF RHAMPHORHYNCHUSES. THEY SWOOP DOWN NOISILY FROM THEIR ROOSTING PLACE.

ARRK!!

KIIARRK!!

KIIARRK!!

THE COELURUSES ARE STILL HUNGRY. THEY SEE THE RHAMPHORHYNCHUSES AND FOLLOW THEM.

THE BRACHIOSAURUS IS THIRSTY AND WALKS TO A NEARBY POOL TO DRINK. THE RHAMPHORHYNCHUSES ARE ALREADY THERE. THEY ARE FISH EATERS AND USE THEIR STRANGELY SHAPED BEAKS AND FORWARD-POINTING TEETH TO SCOOP FISH OUT OF THE WATER.

THE YOUNG BRACHIOSAURUS LOWERS HER HEAD AND DRINKS FROM THE POOL.

WHILE HER HEAD IS NEAR THE GROUND, SHE SWALLOWS A MOUTHFUL OF STONES FROM THE WATER'S EDGE. THE STONES, CALLED GASTROLITHS, HELP DIGEST HER FOOD BY MASHING UP THE TOUGH PLANT LEAVES AND STEMS IN HER STOMACH. WHAT GOES IN...

...MUST COME OUT. THERE ARE STILL SOME **NUTRIENTS** IN THE DINOSAUR'S WASTE. DUNG BEETLES EAT IT, LAY THEIR EGGS IN IT AND BURY IT. THE WASTE ALSO FEEDS THE SOIL.

PART FOUR... THE VALLEY

FROM THE TOP OF A CLIFF, A TORVOSAURUS LOOKS DOWN AT THE FEEDING HERD OF BRACHIOSAURUSES.

THE BRACHIOSAURUS HERD HAS WANDERED INTO A SMALL VALLEY FULL OF CYCADS, PINE TREES AND FERNS.

THE YOUNG BRACHIOSAURUS IS TEN YEARS OLD AND NEARLY HALF GROWN.

WHILE THE BRACHIOSAURUSES **BROWSE** ON THE LUSH VEGETATION, THE TORVOSAURUS CAREFULLY PICKS HIS WAY DOWN THE STEEP VALLEY SIDE.

MEANWHILE, A VIOLENT THUNDERSTORM IS LASHING THE HILLS ABOVE THE VALLEY.

THE TORVOSAURUS REACHES THE BOTTOM OF THE VALLEY. THE BRACHIOSAURUSES HAVE NOT SEEN HIM. THE MEAT EATER IS NOT BIG ENOUGH TO BRING DOWN AN ADULT BRACHIOSAURUS, SO HE LOOKS FOR A JUVENILE.

HE SPOTS THE YOUNG BRACHIOSAURUS.

SUDDENLY, THE TORVOSAURUS DASHES FROM HIS HIDING PLACE. THE BRACHIOSAURUSES RUN IN PANIC WHEN THEY SEE THE LARGE MEAT EATER RUSHING TOWARDS THEM.

ABOVE THE VALLEY, WATER FROM THE STORM FILLS THE STREAMS AND RIVERS...

...AND THEY JOIN TO FORM ONE LARGE **TORRENT** OF WATER.

LOWER DOWN THE VALLEY, THE TORVOSAURUS CATCHES UP WITH THE YOUNG BRACHIOSAURUS...

...AND LEAPS ONTO HER BACK. SHARP TEETH AND CLAWS DIG INTO THE BRACHIOSAURUS'S SKIN.

SHE TRIES HARD TO SHAKE OFF THE HUGE MEAT EATER, BUT HE WILL NOT LET GO.

AS THE TWO BEASTS FIGHT, WATER GUSHES INTO THE VALLEY. THE STORM HAS CREATED A FLOOD.

THE TORVOSAURUS DOES NOT GIVE UP. HE WADES THROUGH THE WATER TOWARDS THE BRACHIOSAURUS.

THERE ARE OTHER THINGS CAUGHT IN THE FLOOD WATERS, BESIDES THE DINOSAURS. A TREE TRUNK SPEEDS TOWARDS THE TWO ANIMALS.

THE TORVOSAURUS NEVER REACHES THE BRACHIOSAURUS. HE IS SWEPT AWAY BY THE FALLEN TREE.

THE BRACHIOSAURUS WADES TO THE RIVERBANK. THE REST OF THE HERD IS SAFE. IN A FEW YEARS, SHE WILL BE TOO BIG FOR EVEN A TORVOSAURUS TO BE A THREAT. UNTIL THEN, SHE WILL STAY AS CLOSE AS SHE CAN TO THE HERD.

FOSSIL EVIDENCE

SCIENTISTS LEARN WHAT DINOSAURS MAY HAVE LOOKED LIKE BY STUDYING THEIR FOSSIL REMAINS. FOSSILS ARE FORMED WHEN THE HARD PARTS OF AN ANIMAL OR PLANT ARE BURIED AND TURN TO ROCK OVER THOUSANDS OF YEARS.

At 12.5 metres, the fossilised Brachiosaurus skeleton in the Humboldt Museum in Berlin, Germany, is the tallest **mounted** skeleton in the world. When it was first put together in 1937, it had an S-shaped neck and its elbows stuck out from its sides.

Since then, scientists have spent more time studying how Brachiosauruses stood and walked. In 2004, the skeleton was taken down and rebuilt. The new mounted skeleton (left) shows Brachiosaurus with a straighter neck and with its elbows tucked into its sides.

Scientists found that Brachiosaurus straightened its neck and lowered its head when it walked, lifting it up again when it stopped. It had to twist its whole neck to turn its head left or right.

ALL THESE ANIMALS APPEAR IN THE STORY.

Rhamphorhynchus
(ram-foh-RINK-us)
'Beak snout'
Wingspan: 2 metres
A small flying reptile that had a long tail and caught fish with its beaked mouth.

Othnielia
(oth-ni-ee-lee-a)
'Othniel's dinosaur'
Length: 1.5 metres
A small, fast-moving plant eater that weighed about 10 kilogrammes.

Coelurus
(seel-YEW-rus)
'Hollow tail'
Length: 2.5 metres
A small meat-eating dinosaur that gets its name from the hollow bones in its tail.

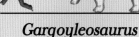

Gargoyleosaurus
(gahr-goy-lee-oh-sore-us)
'Gargoyle lizard'
Length: 3.5 metres
A plant-eating dinosaur that was covered with bony plates for protection.

Torvosaurus
(TOR-voh-SORE-us)
'Savage lizard'
Length: 10 metres
Torvosaurus was the largest known meat eater of the Jurassic period.

Tanycolagreus
(tan-Ee-koh-LAG-ree-us)
'Long-limbed hunter'
Length: 3.5 metres
A meat eater that was a relative of Coelurus. It had long arms and grasping hands.

Marshosaurus
(marsh-oh-sore-us)
'Marsh's lizard'
Length: 5 metres
A meat eater named after the dinosaur hunter Othniel Charles Marsh.

Haplocanthosaurus
(hap-lo-kan-tho-sore-us)
'Simple spined lizard'
Length: 14 metres
Haplocanthosaurus was small compared to other sauropods of its time.

Supersaurus
(sue-per-sore-us)
'Super lizard'
Length: 33 metres
A giant plant-eating dinosaur weighing 31,750 – 36,200 kilogrammes.

Camarasaurus
(KAM-ar-a-sore-us)
'Chambered lizard'
Length: 18 metres
The plant-eating Camarasaurus gets its name from the holes in its skull and backbone.

GLOSSARY

browse	To feed on plants by nibbling here and there.
carcass	The body of a dead animal.
dodge	To avoid an object by moving quickly.
fossils	The remains of living things that have turned to rock.
Jurassic period	The time between 200 million years ago and 145 million years ago.
juvenile	A young animal that is not fully grown.
mounted	Put on show for the public to see.
nutrients	Foods that help living things grow.
torrent	Something flowing in a strong, fast-moving stream.
undergrowth	Low-growing vegetation.

INDEX